PETER AND THE WOLF

A musical tale for children

Serge Prokofieff

Arranged for easy piano by Carol Barratt

Illustrations by Peter Bailey

Verse by Anthony Marks
after an original story by Serge Prokofieff

BOOSEY & HAWKES

Boosey & Hawkes Music Publishers Ltd
www.boosey.com

Ways to use this book

Prokofieff's classic musical tale, written in 1936, is retold here in verse with easy yet faithful arrangements of the main musical themes. The verse makes it ideal for reading aloud, either as a story book or as a performance resource.

Young children will enjoy having the story read to them and the music played; if no pianist is available, the book will form an enchanting visual accompaniment to a recording, as the narrative and pictures closely follow the dramatic line of the original.

Older children will have no difficulty reading the verse themselves, and will also find it easy to memorize and recite. Some of the music can be played by beginners; intermediate players will be able to play it all with relative ease.

Teachers may find it useful to have some pupils read the verse while others play the pieces at the appropriate places. The story will also lend itself to all kinds of interpretations by drama or dance groups.

Additional copies of the text can be downloaded from www.boosey.com/teaching/resources

Introduction

Each character in this story is represented by a different tune. When you hear it played by the orchestra, each tune is played by a different instrument, so each character has its own sound. Here are the characters and their tunes, and the instruments you would hear in the version for orchestra.

Peter's theme is played by the stringed instruments - violins, violas, cellos and double basses.

The bird's theme is played by the flute.

The duck's theme is played by the oboe.

The cat's theme is played by the clarinet.

Grandfather's theme is played by the bassoon.

And the wolf's theme is played by three horns.

Here's a boy whose name is Peter
opening the garden gate.
Out he goes into the meadow -
he doesn't stop, he doesn't wait.

It's still early in the morning,
Lots to do and lots to see,
Peter's friend the bird is singing
in the branches of a tree.

Then a duck comes through the gate,
Looking forward to a swim.
She waddles over to the pond,
One small hop and - splash! - she's in!

Andantino

The bird flies down and shrugs his shoulders -
"You're a bird, but you don't fly!"
The duck sits calmly in the water -
"You can't swim! I wonder why?"

Soon they're squabbling. There's the bird,
hopping up and down the shore.
The duck is paddling in the water
(that's what her webbed feet are for).

Such an awful fuss! Have you
ever heard a noise like that? But
Peter's spotted something crawling
slowly through the grass - a cat!

The cat thinks there's a chance to grab
the quarrelling bird, and so she crawls
towards him on her velvet paws. But
Peter sees - "Look out!" he calls.

All at once the bird flies off,
back to safety in the tree,
and from the middle of the pond
the duck starts quacking angrily.

The cat slinks round and round. She's thinking:
"Is it really worth the climb?
The bird will only fly away.
It's a total waste of time."

Now who's this? It's Peter's Grandpa.
He's not looking very pleased. "You
shouldn't go into the meadow!"
And he points towards the trees.

"You mustn't play out here, you know.
It's too dangerous!" he shouts.
"Wolves live in the forest. You'd be
really scared if one came out!"

Andante

But Peter's not afraid of wolves.
He ignores his Grandpa's words.
He likes playing in the meadow
with his friends, cat, duck and bird.

Andantino

So Grandpa takes him by the hand,
leads him home and locks the gate.
(But Peter wants some more excitement -
He doesn't have too long to wait.)

As soon as they have left the meadow -
Grandpa rattling his keys -
There's a rustle from the forest.
A big grey wolf comes through the trees.

Andante molto

Cat climbs quickly up the branches,

Duck jumps quacking to the shore.
The wolf runs up, the duck runs off,
but can't escape his speeding paws.
He catches her and with a GULP!
He swallows her between his jaws.

So this is how things stand. The cat
sits on one branch and - not too near -
the bird sits on another, while
the wolf licks his lips from ear to ear.

Peter watches from inside,
He doesn't feel the slightest fear.
And suddenly he runs back home
Because he's had a good idea.

He brings a rope and climbs the wall.
(The wolf's still prowling hungrily.)
He grabs hold of a branch and swings
himself up high into the tree.

And then he whispers to his friend
the bird: "Fly down and circle low
around his head! Go on! Be quick!
Make sure he doesn't catch you, though!"

And so the brave bird flutters down,
and flaps around the animal's head,
but every time he snaps his jaws,
the wolf just tastes thin air instead.

The bird is clever, and the wolf
is getting more and more confused.
And meanwhile Peter, in the tree,
has made himself a fine lasso!

He lets it down. It slips around
the animal's tail - he pulls it tight.
The wolf, realising he is caught,
jumps about and tries to fight.

But Peter ties the other end
of his lasso onto the tree.
No matter how the wolf protests,
he's trapped. He simply can't get free.

Here's some huntsmen, guns held high,
Through the forest edge they burst.
They've been following the wolf -
But someone else has caught him first!

Peter's still up in the tree.
"Hey! Don't shoot! You don't need to!
We've already caught the wolf.
Now help us take him to the zoo!"

22

Imagine the procession! Look -
Peter first . . .

. . . the huntsmen next . . .

. . . leading the wolf . . .

. . . and then the cat . . .

. . . and Grandpa (looking very vexed).

The bird is flying high above,
Chirping merrily to the rest,
"See what we did! Aren't we clever!
We caught a wolf! We're the best!"

And if you listen carefully,
You will hear the little duck.
The wolf has swallowed her alive -
Isn't that a piece of luck?

Andante

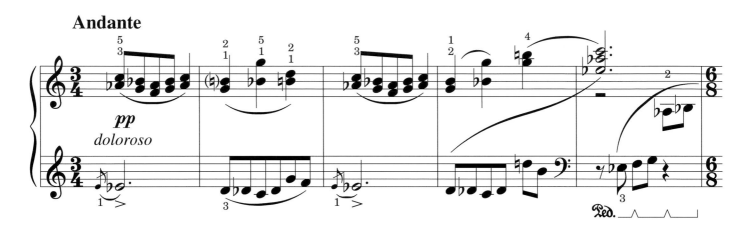

accelerando

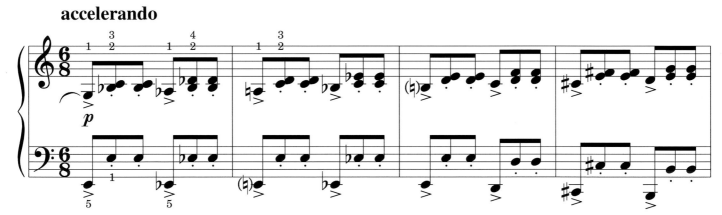

Allegro